Healed

A Guide to Putting the Pieces Back Together
from Being Broken

By Erika Lewis, LCPC, LMHC

A SELF

WORTH

HEALING

This Journal Belongs To

———————————————————

DEDICATED TO EVERY FOSTER CHILD AROUND THE WORLD.

MAY YOU BEGIN TO FIND A PLACE OF HEALING AND LOVE.

KEEP FIGHTING, I SEE YOU!

Table of contents

Song List

- We Fall Down- Donnie McClurkin
- One Wing- Jordan Sparks
- Bag Lady- Erykah Badu
- Song Cry- Jay Z
- Dreams and Nightmares- Meek Mills
- Trip- Ella Mai
- We Can't Be Friends- R. L. and Deborah Cox
- The Storm Is Over Now- God's Property
- Not Gon Cry- Mary J. Blidge
- People- Johnathan McReynolds
- I Told the Storm- Greg O'Quin
- Ex-Factor- Lauryn Hill
- Everybody Mad- O.T. Gensis
- Heartless- Kanye West
- Doo Wop (that thing) – Lauryn Hill
- Friends- The Carters
- Who You Are- Jessie J
- Gonna Be a Lovely Day- Kirk Franklin and The Family
- Best Thing I never Had- Beyoncé
- Level Up- Ciara
- Me, Myself and I- Beyoncé
- I Been- Ari Lennox
- Masterpiece- Jazmine Sullivan
- Gotta Find Peace of Mind- Lauryn Hill

Introduction

This journal is intended for the emotional hoarder. The person who holds onto their baggage and never unpacks. The person who feels that they just cannot go on anymore dealing with the trauma or tired of hitting brick walls and feel like they have had enough. Adversity is inevitable and will continue to happen throughout our lifetime. It is one of those things that will have us questioning and rethinking our overall life trajectory. This journal is intended to help you redirect your way of thinking and to view adversity in a more positive way.

On this journey you will go through the healing process without ignoring any trauma you may have experienced. You may want to skip over some of the toughest pieces and not face what you may be going through, but you have to be open enough to let the healing process begin and serve its purpose for all of your negative experiences and that won't always be easy. Think about it, when you have a wound on your body you must give it time to heal. Sometimes we peel back the scab causing it to bleed, reinjuring ourselves when we were not healed yet and before you know it you have a new scar. This journal will help aide you while going through the healing process attempting to not reinjure those wounds, but to heal them and if a scar is left over, embracing it for something positive.

My hope is that as you go through this journey of healing so that you will learn how to successfully cope with your emotional trauma and baggage. By doing this, you will be more mentally and emotional stable. It will also shed light on how you treat yourself now and how to challenge the way you think about yourself and your life so you can fully operate to best of your abilities and reposition yourself in a new direction. A positive direction that will have you embracing adversity and have a newfound ability to deal with your problems in ways that you were not able to before.

So, embrace yourself and get ready for this ride. One that is meant strictly for you. Healing is personal! Healing isn't about the other person and never is. It's about you and how you process the hurt and what you are willing to do moving forward from the pain. Too often, we focus so much on the how to move forward that we get stuck and don't allow the process even to begin, more or less to let it simply work itself out. Instead, we will focus on creating open communication with the pain, get it to hear us, and get the pain to change for us. To channel positive energy inward and focus on how we can learn and grow from adversity and heal in such a way to be a stronger, wiser, and better person.

Often times when we are dealing with adversity, we want to skip it because it makes us uncomfortable or we try to find some way to avoid dealing with it completely. Truth is, life is made up of experiences, both the good and the bad, and they all help us grow. The problem we find ourselves in is that the bad ones make us want to shut down and not work on what is bothering us. We must push ourselves to go through the process no matter how tough or difficult it may be. You may have heard the saying, "What doesn't kill you will only make you stronger." That is indeed true, but it is also how you look at your circumstances that will make you stronger. For many of us, adversity can be very difficult to even know where to start, especially if we don't have the right outlook or attitude about it.

In this journal you will have blank spaces to share your thoughts and write down your feelings. There is also music that I selected for you to meditate on and use as one of the coping mechanisms to help you heal and to feel the emotions. In addition, there will be empowering quotes throughout the book, and I hope that you are able to repeat them out loud or to yourself and discuss what they mean to you. It all starts with you. Healing starts with you. Heal thyself so that you can be your healthy self.

"I hope you heal"

Hurt

Introspection

What would you like to heal from? What impact has it had on you?

_____

_____

_____

_____

_____

_____

_____

_____

_____

_____

_____

_____

_____

_____

_____

_____

Morning Thoughts

Today, I woke up feeling like:

Today, in my healing process I want to unpack:

I can process this issue by doing:

I know that I cannot change anyone else and I only have the power to change myself. I can work on myself by doing the following:

A positive affirmation I can use throughout the day is:

Daytime Thoughts

Currently I feel:

Today, I am struggling with:

Coping mechanism and the people who supported me today:

Nighttime Thoughts

Overall, I had a (blank) type of day:

Did anything negative happen today?

How did I handle it and if I handled it negatively could I have done something different?

I can go to bed and think positive by doing the follow:

My nighttime positive affirmation is:

"I am healing"

Morning Thoughts

Date: /   /

Today, I woke up feeling like:

Today, in my healing process I want to unpack:

I can process this issue by doing:

I know that I cannot change anyone else and I only have the power to change myself. I can work on myself by doing the following:

A positive affirmation I can use throughout the day is:

Daytime Thoughts

Currently I feel:

Today, I am struggling with:

Coping mechanism and the people who supported me today:

Nighttime Thoughts

Overall, I had a (blank) type of day:

Did anything negative happen today?

How did I handle it and if I handled it negatively could I have done something different?

I can go to bed and think positive by doing the follow:

My nighttime positive affirmation is:

"I am healing"

Morning Thoughts

Today, I woke up feeling like:

Today, in my healing process I want to unpack:

I can process this issue by doing:

I know that I cannot change anyone else and I only have the power to change myself. I can work on myself by doing the following:

A positive affirmation I can use throughout the day is:

Daytime Thoughts

Currently I feel:

Today, I am struggling with:

Coping mechanism and the people who supported me today:

Nighttime Thoughts

Overall, I had a (blank) type of day:

Did anything negative happen today?

How did I handle it and if I handled it negatively could I have done something different?

I can go to bed and think positive by doing the follow:

My nighttime positive affirmation is:

"I am healing"

Morning Thoughts

Today, I woke up feeling like:

Today, in my healing process I want to unpack:

I can process this issue by doing:

I know that I cannot change anyone else and I only have the power to change myself. I can work on myself by doing the following:

A positive affirmation I can use throughout the day is:

Daytime Thoughts

Currently I feel:

Today, I am struggling with:

Coping mechanism and the people who supported me today:

Nighttime Thoughts

Overall, I had a (blank) type of day:

Did anything negative happen today?

How did I handle it and if I handled it negatively could I have done something different?

I can go to bed and think positive by doing the follow:

My nighttime positive affirmation is:

"I am healing"

Morning Thoughts

Date: /   /

Today, I woke up feeling like:

Today, in my healing process I want to unpack:

I can process this issue by doing:

I know that I cannot change anyone else and I only have the power to change myself. I can work on myself by doing the following:

A positive affirmation I can use throughout the day is:

Daytime Thoughts

Currently I feel:

Today, I am struggling with:

Coping mechanism and the people who supported me today:

Nighttime Thoughts

Overall, I had a (blank) type of day:

Did anything negative happen today?

How did I handle it and if I handled it negatively could I have done something different?

I can go to bed and think positive by doing the follow:

My nighttime positive affirmation is:

"I am healing"

You can't heal just pieces of you to get better. You have to heal all of you or nothing at all.

The healing process can be one that is very daunting at times, sometimes even too hard to face. Moreover, the healing process is not up for you to decide what parts you want to heal because that's what easiest for you. You have to be open to welcome the process. Pain comes but it also goes. It's temporary like our emotions. But it can feel permanent if we don't get clear about our intentions with our healing. It's easy to work on parts of you that you can change at a drop of a hat, but what about the other part? The part that you have to fight to mend back together, heal that too. Because just healing pieces of you will always leave you feeling broken and not whole. So be very clear about what it takes for you to move on from brokenness and develop an action plan so that you can start doing the work.

"Once I healed I never looked back."

Introspection

What's in your suitcase?

_____

_____

_____

_____

_____

_____

_____

List everything that is bothering you below.

_____

_____

_____

_____

_____

_____

_____

_____

_____

Morning Thoughts

Date: _____ / _____ / _____

Today, I woke up feeling like:

Today, in my healing process I want to unpack:

I can process this issue by doing:

I know that I cannot change anyone else and I only have the power to change myself. I can work on myself by doing the following:

A positive affirmation I can use throughout the day is:

Daytime Thoughts

Currently I feel:

Today, I am struggling with:

Coping mechanism and the people who supported me today:

Nighttime Thoughts

Overall, I had a (blank) type of day:

Did anything negative happen today?

How did I handle it and if I handled it negatively could I have done something different?

I can go to bed and think positive by doing the follow:

My nighttime positive affirmation is:

"I am healing"

Morning Thoughts

Today, I woke up feeling like:

Today, in my healing process I want to unpack:

I can process this issue by doing:

I know that I cannot change anyone else and I only have the power to change myself. I can work on myself by doing the following:

A positive affirmation I can use throughout the day is:

Daytime Thoughts

Currently I feel:

Today, I am struggling with:

Coping mechanism and the people who supported me today:

Nighttime Thoughts

Overall, I had a (blank) type of day:

Did anything negative happen today?

How did I handle it and if I handled it negatively could I have done something different?

I can go to bed and think positive by doing the follow:

My nighttime positive affirmation is:

"I am healing"

Morning Thoughts

Today, I woke up feeling like:

Today, in my healing process I want to unpack:

I can process this issue by doing:

I know that I cannot change anyone else and I only have the power to change myself. I can work on myself by doing the following:

A positive affirmation I can use throughout the day is:

Daytime Thoughts

Currently I feel:

Today, I am struggling with:

Coping mechanism and the people who supported me today:

Nighttime Thoughts

Overall, I had a (blank) type of day:

Did anything negative happen today?

How did I handle it and if I handled it negatively could I have done something different?

I can go to bed and think positive by doing the follow:

My nighttime positive affirmation is:

"I am healing"

Morning Thoughts

Today, I woke up feeling like:

Today, in my healing process I want to unpack:

I can process this issue by doing:

I know that I cannot change anyone else and I only have the power to change myself.
I can work on myself by doing the following:

A positive affirmation I can use throughout the day is:

Daytime Thoughts

Currently I feel:

Today, I am struggling with:

Coping mechanism and the people who supported me today:

Nighttime Thoughts

Overall, I had a (blank) type of day:

Did anything negative happen today?

How did I handle it and if I handled it negatively could I have done something different?

I can go to bed and think positive by doing the follow:

My nighttime positive affirmation is:

"I am healing"

Morning Thoughts

Date: /   /

Today, I woke up feeling like:

Today, in my healing process I want to unpack:

I can process this issue by doing:

I know that I cannot change anyone else and I only have the power to change myself. I can work on myself by doing the following:

A positive affirmation I can use throughout the day is:

Daytime Thoughts

Currently I feel:

Today, I am struggling with:

Coping mechanism and the people who supported me today:

Nighttime Thoughts

Overall, I had a (blank) type of day:

Did anything negative happen today?

How did I handle it and if I handled it negatively could I have done something different?

I can go to bed and think positive by doing the follow:

My nighttime positive affirmation is:

"I am healing"

Don't allow someone to tell you who you are... You write the narrative to your story.

People are so quick to offer you their unsolicited opinions on who they think that you are or what they think the issue(s) might be—and you may fall victim to it. Reason being is that; you might not have a true sense of who you are or the situation. So you may let others write the narrative to your story, leaving you left with a bunch of alternative facts and distorted half-truths. Don't let anyone tell you who they think you are or what the story may be. Start looking deeper into yourself and gain a greater sense of who you are and the situation. So that when people form their opinions an offer them to you, you're not easily impressed.

"My fight to heal is unmatched;
I will win no matter how many times I fall."

Introspection

What was it that broke you?

_____

_____

_____

_____

_____

_____

What did that feel like?

_____

_____

_____

_____

_____

_____

How do you feel now that you are writing about it?

_____

_____

_____

_____

_____

_____

Morning Thoughts

Today, I woke up feeling like:

Today, in my healing process I want to unpack:

I can process this issue by doing:

I know that I cannot change anyone else and I only have the power to change myself. I can work on myself by doing the following:

A positive affirmation I can use throughout the day is:

Daytime Thoughts

Currently I feel:

Today, I am struggling with:

Coping mechanism and the people who supported me today:

Nighttime Thoughts

Overall, I had a (blank) type of day:

Did anything negative happen today?

How did I handle it and if I handled it negatively could I have done something different?

I can go to bed and think positive by doing the follow:

My nighttime positive affirmation is:

"I am healing"

Morning Thoughts

Today, I woke up feeling like:

Today, in my healing process I want to unpack:

I can process this issue by doing:

I know that I cannot change anyone else and I only have the power to change myself. I can work on myself by doing the following:

A positive affirmation I can use throughout the day is:

Daytime Thoughts

Currently I feel:

Today, I am struggling with:

Coping mechanism and the people who supported me today:

Nighttime Thoughts

Overall, I had a (blank) type of day:

Did anything negative happen today?

How did I handle it and if I handled it negatively could I have done something different?

I can go to bed and think positive by doing the follow:

My nighttime positive affirmation is:

"I am healing"

Morning Thoughts

Today, I woke up feeling like:

Today, in my healing process I want to unpack:

I can process this issue by doing:

I know that I cannot change anyone else and I only have the power to change myself. I can work on myself by doing the following:

A positive affirmation I can use throughout the day is:

Daytime Thoughts

Currently I feel:

Today, I am struggling with:

Coping mechanism and the people who supported me today:

Nighttime Thoughts

Overall, I had a (blank) type of day:

Did anything negative happen today?

How did I handle it and if I handled it negatively could I have done something different?

I can go to bed and think positive by doing the follow:

My nighttime positive affirmation is:

"I am healing"

Morning Thoughts

Today, I woke up feeling like:

Today, in my healing process I want to unpack:

I can process this issue by doing:

I know that I cannot change anyone else and I only have the power to change myself.
I can work on myself by doing the following:

A positive affirmation I can use throughout the day is:

Daytime Thoughts

Currently I feel:

Today, I am struggling with:

Coping mechanism and the people who supported me today:

Nighttime Thoughts

Overall, I had a (blank) type of day:

Did anything negative happen today?

How did I handle it and if I handled it negatively could I have done something different?

I can go to bed and think positive by doing the follow:

My nighttime positive affirmation is:

"I am healing"

Morning Thoughts

Today, I woke up feeling like:

Today, in my healing process I want to unpack:

I can process this issue by doing:

I know that I cannot change anyone else and I only have the power to change myself. I can work on myself by doing the following:

A positive affirmation I can use throughout the day is:

Daytime Thoughts

Currently I feel:

Today, I am struggling with:

Coping mechanism and the people who supported me today:

Nighttime Thoughts

Overall, I had a (blank) type of day:

Did anything negative happen today?

How did I handle it and if I handled it negatively could I have done something different?

I can go to bed and think positive by doing the follow:

My nighttime positive affirmation is:

"I am healing"

Stop waiting for a breakthrough and let go of what's breaking you!

Too many of us are waiting for a breakthrough but won't let go of what's breaking you. If you let go of that negative attachment that has been weighing you down, holding you back, and preventing you from pushing forward. You might just be open enough to see you don't need a breakthrough to get you through what you need to let go.

"I'm going to get through."

Introspection

What are some things that are breaking you? How can you remove those things that are breaking you?

_____

_____

_____

_____

_____

_____

_____

_____

_____

_____

_____

_____

_____

_____

_____

_____

_____

Morning Thoughts

Today, I woke up feeling like:

Today, in my healing process I want to unpack:

I can process this issue by doing:

I know that I cannot change anyone else and I only have the power to change myself. I can work on myself by doing the following:

A positive affirmation I can use throughout the day is:

Daytime Thoughts

Currently I feel:

Today, I am struggling with:

Coping mechanism and the people who supported me today:

Nighttime Thoughts

Overall, I had a (blank) type of day:

Did anything negative happen today?

How did I handle it and if I handled it negatively could I have done something different?

I can go to bed and think positive by doing the follow:

My nighttime positive affirmation is:

"I am healing"

Morning Thoughts

Today, I woke up feeling like:

Today, in my healing process I want to unpack:

I can process this issue by doing:

I know that I cannot change anyone else and I only have the power to change myself. I can work on myself by doing the following:

A positive affirmation I can use throughout the day is:

Daytime Thoughts

Currently I feel:

Today, I am struggling with:

Coping mechanism and the people who supported me today:

Nighttime Thoughts

Overall, I had a (blank) type of day:

Did anything negative happen today?

How did I handle it and if I handled it negatively could I have done something different?

I can go to bed and think positive by doing the follow:

My nighttime positive affirmation is:

"I am healing"

Morning Thoughts

Today, I woke up feeling like:

Today, in my healing process I want to unpack:

I can process this issue by doing:

I know that I cannot change anyone else and I only have the power to change myself. I can work on myself by doing the following:

A positive affirmation I can use throughout the day is:

Daytime Thoughts

Currently I feel:

Today, I am struggling with:

Coping mechanism and the people who supported me today:

Nighttime Thoughts

Overall, I had a (blank) type of day:

Did anything negative happen today?

How did I handle it and if I handled it negatively could I have done something different?

I can go to bed and think positive by doing the follow:

My nighttime positive affirmation is:

"I am healing"

Morning Thoughts

Today, I woke up feeling like:

Today, in my healing process I want to unpack:

I can process this issue by doing:

I know that I cannot change anyone else and I only have the power to change myself. I can work on myself by doing the following:

A positive affirmation I can use throughout the day is:

Daytime Thoughts

Currently I feel:

Today, I am struggling with:

Coping mechanism and the people who supported me today:

Nighttime Thoughts

Overall, I had a (blank) type of day:

Did anything negative happen today?

How did I handle it and if I handled it negatively could I have done something different?

I can go to bed and think positive by doing the follow:

My nighttime positive affirmation is:

"I am healing"

Morning Thoughts

Date: /   /

Today, I woke up feeling like:

Today, in my healing process I want to unpack:

I can process this issue by doing:

I know that I cannot change anyone else and I only have the power to change myself. I can work on myself by doing the following:

A positive affirmation I can use throughout the day is:

Daytime Thoughts

Currently I feel:

Today, I am struggling with:

Coping mechanism and the people who supported me today:

Nighttime Thoughts

Overall, I had a (blank) type of day:

Did anything negative happen today?

How did I handle it and if I handled it negatively could I have done something different?

I can go to bed and think positive by doing the follow:

My nighttime positive affirmation is:

"I am healing"

Don't expect someone to choose you, if you don't choose yourself.

How often are you choosing yourself? How often are you saying yes to you? We crave love, we naturally want to feel wanted by others, chosen by others and to have that sense of belongingness. Whether it's with your relationships or a job, say yes to you! Give yourself the same chance you want someone to give you. Love yourself just as hard as you want someone to love you. And most importantly choose you, even when you're not chosen! We know how to be there for others but sometimes you have to be everything for you, not just them! So often we neglect to care for ourselves because we are too busy caring for everyone else. It's time to give back to yourself—because right now you need YOU! How would you be able to give your time and care to someone else if you're not okay and struggling yourself? Start by identifying ways in which you can show up for you and be more present in your own life.

"Healing starts with you."

Introspection

How can you be more present and show up for yourself?

_____

_____

_____

_____

_____

_____

_____

_____

_____

_____

_____

_____

_____

_____

_____

_____

_____

Morning Thoughts

Today, I woke up feeling like:

Today, in my healing process I want to unpack:

I can process this issue by doing:

I know that I cannot change anyone else and I only have the power to change myself.
I can work on myself by doing the following:

A positive affirmation I can use throughout the day is:

Daytime Thoughts

Currently I feel:

Today, I am struggling with:

Coping mechanism and the people who supported me today:

Nighttime Thoughts

Overall, I had a (blank) type of day:

Did anything negative happen today?

How did I handle it and if I handled it negatively could I have done something different?

I can go to bed and think positive by doing the follow:

My nighttime positive affirmation is:

"I am healing"

Morning Thoughts

Today, I woke up feeling like:

Today, in my healing process I want to unpack:

I can process this issue by doing:

I know that I cannot change anyone else and I only have the power to change myself. I can work on myself by doing the following:

A positive affirmation I can use throughout the day is:

Daytime Thoughts

Currently I feel:

Today, I am struggling with:

Coping mechanism and the people who supported me today:

Nighttime Thoughts

Overall, I had a (blank) type of day:

Did anything negative happen today?

How did I handle it and if I handled it negatively could I have done something different?

I can go to bed and think positive by doing the follow:

My nighttime positive affirmation is:

"I am healing"

Morning Thoughts

Date:	/	/

Today, I woke up feeling like:

Today, in my healing process I want to unpack:

I can process this issue by doing:

I know that I cannot change anyone else and I only have the power to change myself. I can work on myself by doing the following:

A positive affirmation I can use throughout the day is:

Daytime Thoughts

Currently I feel:

Today, I am struggling with:

Coping mechanism and the people who supported me today:

Nighttime Thoughts

Overall, I had a (blank) type of day:

Did anything negative happen today?

How did I handle it and if I handled it negatively could I have done something different?

I can go to bed and think positive by doing the follow:

My nighttime positive affirmation is:

"I am healing"

Morning Thoughts

Today, I woke up feeling like:

Today, in my healing process I want to unpack:

I can process this issue by doing:

I know that I cannot change anyone else and I only have the power to change myself. I can work on myself by doing the following:

A positive affirmation I can use throughout the day is:

Daytime Thoughts

Currently I feel:

Today, I am struggling with:

Coping mechanism and the people who supported me today:

Nighttime Thoughts

Overall, I had a (blank) type of day:

Did anything negative happen today?

How did I handle it and if I handled it negatively could I have done something different?

I can go to bed and think positive by doing the follow:

My nighttime positive affirmation is:

"I am healing"

Morning Thoughts

Today, I woke up feeling like:

Today, in my healing process I want to unpack:

I can process this issue by doing:

I know that I cannot change anyone else and I only have the power to change myself.
I can work on myself by doing the following:

A positive affirmation I can use throughout the day is:

Daytime Thoughts

Currently I feel:

Today, I am struggling with:

Coping mechanism and the people who supported me today:

Nighttime Thoughts

Overall, I had a (blank) type of day:

Did anything negative happen today?

How did I handle it and if I handled it negatively could I have done something different?

I can go to bed and think positive by doing the follow:

My nighttime positive affirmation is:

"I am healing"

A relationship can't heal you especially if you enter into it broken.

Not many people understand that entering into a relationship complete and whole within you is so important to keep a relationship healthy and thriving. It is not your partner's responsibility to make you happy and whole. You have to come into the relationship ready and equipped to handle all aspects of that relationship. Being mentally, emotionally, spiritually, and financially stable are must haves before entering into any relationship. Think about the qualities you possess beforehand. And if you're not in a relationship or have never been in one, start to have the conversation with self about what that will look like for you and how can show up and be present but complete and whole at the same time.

"Even a broken wing can heal."

Introspection

In what ways have you tried to use a relationship in order to fill a void in your life?

_____

_____

_____

_____

_____

_____

_____

_____

_____

_____

_____

_____

_____

_____

_____

_____

_____

Morning Thoughts

Date: /   /

Today, I woke up feeling like:

Today, in my healing process I want to unpack:

I can process this issue by doing:

I know that I cannot change anyone else and I only have the power to change myself. I can work on myself by doing the following:

A positive affirmation I can use throughout the day is:

Daytime Thoughts

Currently I feel:

Today, I am struggling with:

Coping mechanism and the people who supported me today:

Nighttime Thoughts

Overall, I had a (blank) type of day:

Did anything negative happen today?

How did I handle it and if I handled it negatively could I have done something different?

I can go to bed and think positive by doing the follow:

My nighttime positive affirmation is:

"I am healing"

Morning Thoughts

Date: /   /

Today, I woke up feeling like:

Today, in my healing process I want to unpack:

I can process this issue by doing:

I know that I cannot change anyone else and I only have the power to change myself. I can work on myself by doing the following:

A positive affirmation I can use throughout the day is:

Daytime Thoughts

Currently I feel:

Today, I am struggling with:

Coping mechanism and the people who supported me today:

Nighttime Thoughts

Overall, I had a (blank) type of day:

Did anything negative happen today?

How did I handle it and if I handled it negatively could I have done something different?

I can go to bed and think positive by doing the follow:

My nighttime positive affirmation is:

"I am healing"

Morning Thoughts

Today, I woke up feeling like:

Today, in my healing process I want to unpack:

I can process this issue by doing:

I know that I cannot change anyone else and I only have the power to change myself. I can work on myself by doing the following:

A positive affirmation I can use throughout the day is:

Daytime Thoughts

Currently I feel:

Today, I am struggling with:

Coping mechanism and the people who supported me today:

Nighttime Thoughts

Overall, I had a (blank) type of day:

Did anything negative happen today?

How did I handle it and if I handled it negatively could I have done something different?

I can go to bed and think positive by doing the follow:

My nighttime positive affirmation is:

"I am healing"

Morning Thoughts

Today, I woke up feeling like:

Today, in my healing process I want to unpack:

I can process this issue by doing:

I know that I cannot change anyone else and I only have the power to change myself. I can work on myself by doing the following:

A positive affirmation I can use throughout the day is:

Daytime Thoughts

Currently I feel:

Today, I am struggling with:

Coping mechanism and the people who supported me today:

Nighttime Thoughts

Overall, I had a (blank) type of day:

Did anything negative happen today?

How did I handle it and if I handled it negatively could I have done something different?

I can go to bed and think positive by doing the follow:

My nighttime positive affirmation is:

"I am healing"

Morning Thoughts

Today, I woke up feeling like:

Today, in my healing process I want to unpack:

I can process this issue by doing:

I know that I cannot change anyone else and I only have the power to change myself. I can work on myself by doing the following:

A positive affirmation I can use throughout the day is:

Daytime Thoughts

Currently I feel:

Today, I am struggling with:

Coping mechanism and the people who supported me today:

Nighttime Thoughts

Overall, I had a (blank) type of day:

Did anything negative happen today?

How did I handle it and if I handled it negatively could I have done something different?

I can go to bed and think positive by doing the follow:

My nighttime positive affirmation is:

"I am healing"

Always remember you're worth it.

D on't spend a lot of time overthinking what was, what could have been, and what should of been. Think about what it is right now! And if right now isn't fitting in what you need or want, then move around. Don't stay stuck in something because you feel things will get better. You are better, and you're worthy of having more, right now. So if things don't come to you with a right now attitude—then it's not for you. Because you deserve the best and you're more than worthy to receive it. But always remember everything isn't for everybody. Yes, patience is of virtue and for somethings we know they may take time to receive. However, when it comes to relationships that we enter into (be it personal or professional) who wants to wait around to be treated right. Always, Always, remember you are worth a right now attitude.

"Time spent doesn't mean a thing it's the quality of the time spent that matters the most."

I can't wait around for you to get your stuff together, because waiting around for you may mean losing me! And we both know that can't happen.

Morning Thoughts

Today, I woke up feeling like:

Today, in my healing process I want to unpack:

I can process this issue by doing:

I know that I cannot change anyone else and I only have the power to change myself. I can work on myself by doing the following:

A positive affirmation I can use throughout the day is:

Daytime Thoughts

Currently I feel:

Today, I am struggling with:

Coping mechanism and the people who supported me today:

Nighttime Thoughts

Overall, I had a (blank) type of day:

Did anything negative happen today?

How did I handle it and if I handled it negatively could I have done something different?

I can go to bed and think positive by doing the follow:

My nighttime positive affirmation is:

"I am healing"

Morning Thoughts

Today, I woke up feeling like:

Today, in my healing process I want to unpack:

I can process this issue by doing:

I know that I cannot change anyone else and I only have the power to change myself. I can work on myself by doing the following:

A positive affirmation I can use throughout the day is:

Daytime Thoughts

Currently I feel:

Today, I am struggling with:

Coping mechanism and the people who supported me today:

Nighttime Thoughts

Overall, I had a (blank) type of day:

Did anything negative happen today?

How did I handle it and if I handled it negatively could I have done something different?

I can go to bed and think positive by doing the follow:

My nighttime positive affirmation is:

"I am healing"

Morning Thoughts

Today, I woke up feeling like:

Today, in my healing process I want to unpack:

I can process this issue by doing:

I know that I cannot change anyone else and I only have the power to change myself. I can work on myself by doing the following:

A positive affirmation I can use throughout the day is:

Daytime Thoughts

Currently I feel:

Today, I am struggling with:

Coping mechanism and the people who supported me today:

Nighttime Thoughts

Overall, I had a (blank) type of day:

Did anything negative happen today?

How did I handle it and if I handled it negatively could I have done something different?

I can go to bed and think positive by doing the follow:

My nighttime positive affirmation is:

"I am healing"

Morning Thoughts

Date:　　　/　　　/

Today, I woke up feeling like:

Today, in my healing process I want to unpack:

I can process this issue by doing:

I know that I cannot change anyone else and I only have the power to change myself. I can work on myself by doing the following:

A positive affirmation I can use throughout the day is:

Daytime Thoughts

Currently I feel:

Today, I am struggling with:

Coping mechanism and the people who supported me today:

Nighttime Thoughts

Overall, I had a (blank) type of day:

Did anything negative happen today?

How did I handle it and if I handled it negatively could I have done something different?

I can go to bed and think positive by doing the follow:

My nighttime positive affirmation is:

"I am healing"

Morning Thoughts

Today, I woke up feeling like:

Today, in my healing process I want to unpack:

I can process this issue by doing:

I know that I cannot change anyone else and I only have the power to change myself. I can work on myself by doing the following:

A positive affirmation I can use throughout the day is:

Daytime Thoughts

Currently I feel:

Today, I am struggling with:

Coping mechanism and the people who supported me today:

Nighttime Thoughts

Overall, I had a (blank) type of day:

Did anything negative happen today?

How did I handle it and if I handled it negatively could I have done something different?

I can go to bed and think positive by doing the follow:

My nighttime positive affirmation is:

"I am healing"

Focusing on other people takes away your ability to see what's ahead.

How often are you looking at what someone else has or is doing? How much of your attention is focused on someone else? Looking to your left and right so much that you completely stop looking ahead? That's how you end up staying distracted and stuck in the same rut. Start redirecting your energy toward what's in front of you and change the trajectory of your thoughts so that you can finally move forward. Be the shift, be the change, be all that you can be. Just don't be the one left behind because you are envious about what someone else is doing! So often we compare ourselves to other people, with what they may have, what they may be doing, and how they are doing it. You may even feel that things that have been hard for you may come easy to others. You may even struggle with the understanding that you might have to work a little bit harder than someone else just to get to the same place, and that is okay. Your path is your path and your story is your story. Tunnel vision on your own goals is what you need to do.

"Winning is about moving forward
and never looking back."

Introspection

Talk about how you can focus more on yourself.

_____

_____

_____

_____

_____

_____

_____

_____

_____

_____

_____

_____

_____

_____

_____

_____

_____

_____

_____

Morning Thoughts

Date: /   /

Today, I woke up feeling like:

Today, in my healing process I want to unpack:

I can process this issue by doing:

I know that I cannot change anyone else and I only have the power to change myself.
I can work on myself by doing the following:

A positive affirmation I can use throughout the day is:

Daytime Thoughts

Currently I feel:

Today, I am struggling with:

Coping mechanism and the people who supported me today:

Nighttime Thoughts

Overall, I had a (blank) type of day:

Did anything negative happen today?

How did I handle it and if I handled it negatively could I have done something different?

I can go to bed and think positive by doing the follow:

My nighttime positive affirmation is:

"I am healing"

Morning Thoughts

Today, I woke up feeling like:

Today, in my healing process I want to unpack:

I can process this issue by doing:

I know that I cannot change anyone else and I only have the power to change myself. I can work on myself by doing the following:

A positive affirmation I can use throughout the day is:

Daytime Thoughts

Currently I feel:

Today, I am struggling with:

Coping mechanism and the people who supported me today:

Nighttime Thoughts

Overall, I had a (blank) type of day:

Did anything negative happen today?

How did I handle it and if I handled it negatively could I have done something different?

I can go to bed and think positive by doing the follow:

My nighttime positive affirmation is:

"I am healing"

Morning Thoughts

Today, I woke up feeling like:

Today, in my healing process I want to unpack:

I can process this issue by doing:

I know that I cannot change anyone else and I only have the power to change myself. I can work on myself by doing the following:

A positive affirmation I can use throughout the day is:

Daytime Thoughts

Currently I feel:

Today, I am struggling with:

Coping mechanism and the people who supported me today:

Nighttime Thoughts

Overall, I had a (blank) type of day:

Did anything negative happen today?

How did I handle it and if I handled it negatively could I have done something different?

I can go to bed and think positive by doing the follow:

My nighttime positive affirmation is:

"I am healing"

Morning Thoughts

Today, I woke up feeling like:

Today, in my healing process I want to unpack:

I can process this issue by doing:

I know that I cannot change anyone else and I only have the power to change myself. I can work on myself by doing the following:

A positive affirmation I can use throughout the day is:

Daytime Thoughts

Currently I feel:

Today, I am struggling with:

Coping mechanism and the people who supported me today:

Nighttime Thoughts

Overall, I had a (blank) type of day:

Did anything negative happen today?

How did I handle it and if I handled it negatively could I have done something different?

I can go to bed and think positive by doing the follow:

My nighttime positive affirmation is:

"I am healing"

Morning Thoughts

Today, I woke up feeling like:

Today, in my healing process I want to unpack:

I can process this issue by doing:

I know that I cannot change anyone else and I only have the power to change myself. I can work on myself by doing the following:

A positive affirmation I can use throughout the day is:

Daytime Thoughts

Currently I feel:

Today, I am struggling with:

Coping mechanism and the people who supported me today:

Nighttime Thoughts

Overall, I had a (blank) type of day:

Did anything negative happen today?

How did I handle it and if I handled it negatively could I have done something different?

I can go to bed and think positive by doing the follow:

My nighttime positive affirmation is:

"I am healing"

Protect yourself at all times.

We grow up being told to protect ourselves at all times, to keep from being physically harmed. But something is missing. What must be included is the need to also protect ourselves from mental harm as well. Sometimes, people come into our lives to mess things up, distort our thinking, and manage to disrupt our lives and our minds. We end up having to face pain, endure hardship and breakthrough mental stress because of those negative and toxic people or events. So, what stops us from protecting the mental and emotional side of ourselves? There's a difference between just putting our guard up and successfully protecting our mental health! So much of the world affects our mental health and we don't even realize it. Part of the issue is that people have a funny way of playing victim to circumstances they have created themselves. So be mindful and protect yourself as much as you can within your control.

Mind what you entertain yourself with. You don't want your mind polluted by something that is so easy to avoid by just changing a channel. When you are trying to heal you want to avoid negative entertainment. Avoid overly violent, sexual, or emotionally charged stimuli. If watching the news or politics makes you angry, give it a break. If there is a movie or show you connect with in a very strong and emotional way, avoid that too. Plenty of masterful tv shows come to mind that are very violent, both with fights or battles and sexually violent as well. You want to try to avoid those while trying to heal your mind. They will be there when you are ready and won't be so affected by them.

Consider your home. Is it messy and cluttered? Is there anyway to clean it out, simplify, and rearrange in such a way to give yourself physical space? Is there physical baggage and items you can do without? Items that remind you of a past event or person that brings a negative emotional response? Clean it out and get rid of it. For many that physical act of cleaning house also cleans and creates space in the mind and serves as a form of meditation even. Try it out and see how it makes you feel.

Finally, be careful of who you allow into your life at this time. If you already know them as someone who makes you uncomfortable, or you know they are a user, toxic, or negative, just tell them you are working some things out and can't see them right now. Remove them from your life completely if need be. If they can't be there for you and simply suck your energy, then you have to find a way and the courage in yourself to cut them off, even if they are family. If they are hurting you they don't deserve your attention or energy.

This is also why you should be wary of meeting new people during this time. You don't have to entirely close that off as you will want good people to replace those you have to cut out, but be sure you get to know them before letting them in. don't feel bad about being picky. It is a well known saying that you become like the people around you, so you need to go out and find those that you want to become.

"I'll never apologize for choosing what's best for me."

Introspection

Is there anyone or anything in your life that causes you mental harm? How can you protect yourself from being mentally harmed by them or it? Tell me your action plan.

_____

_____

_____

_____

_____

_____

_____

_____

_____

_____

_____

_____

_____

_____

_____

_____

_____

Morning Thoughts

Today, I woke up feeling like:

Today, in my healing process I want to unpack:

I can process this issue by doing:

I know that I cannot change anyone else and I only have the power to change myself. I can work on myself by doing the following:

A positive affirmation I can use throughout the day is:

Daytime Thoughts

Currently I feel:

Today, I am struggling with:

Coping mechanism and the people who supported me today:

Nighttime Thoughts

Overall, I had a (blank) type of day:

Did anything negative happen today?

How did I handle it and if I handled it negatively could I have done something different?

I can go to bed and think positive by doing the follow:

My nighttime positive affirmation is:

"I am healing"

Morning Thoughts

Today, I woke up feeling like:

Today, in my healing process I want to unpack:

I can process this issue by doing:

I know that I cannot change anyone else and I only have the power to change myself. I can work on myself by doing the following:

A positive affirmation I can use throughout the day is:

Daytime Thoughts

Currently I feel:

Today, I am struggling with:

Coping mechanism and the people who supported me today:

Nighttime Thoughts

Overall, I had a (blank) type of day:

Did anything negative happen today?

How did I handle it and if I handled it negatively could I have done something different?

I can go to bed and think positive by doing the follow:

My nighttime positive affirmation is:

"I am healing"

Morning Thoughts

Date: /   /

Today, I woke up feeling like:

Today, in my healing process I want to unpack:

I can process this issue by doing:

I know that I cannot change anyone else and I only have the power to change myself. I can work on myself by doing the following:

A positive affirmation I can use throughout the day is:

Daytime Thoughts

Currently I feel:

Today, I am struggling with:

Coping mechanism and the people who supported me today:

Nighttime Thoughts

Overall, I had a (blank) type of day:

Did anything negative happen today?

How did I handle it and if I handled it negatively could I have done something different?

I can go to bed and think positive by doing the follow:

My nighttime positive affirmation is:

"I am healing"

Morning Thoughts

Date: /   /

Today, I woke up feeling like:

Today, in my healing process I want to unpack:

I can process this issue by doing:

I know that I cannot change anyone else and I only have the power to change myself. I can work on myself by doing the following:

A positive affirmation I can use throughout the day is:

Daytime Thoughts

Currently I feel:

Today, I am struggling with:

Coping mechanism and the people who supported me today:

Nighttime Thoughts

Overall, I had a (blank) type of day:

Did anything negative happen today?

How did I handle it and if I handled it negatively could I have done something different?

I can go to bed and think positive by doing the follow:

My nighttime positive affirmation is:

"I am healing"

Morning Thoughts

Date: /   /

Today, I woke up feeling like:

Today, in my healing process I want to unpack:

I can process this issue by doing:

I know that I cannot change anyone else and I only have the power to change myself.
I can work on myself by doing the following:

A positive affirmation I can use throughout the day is:

Daytime Thoughts

Currently I feel:

Today, I am struggling with:

Coping mechanism and the people who supported me today:

Nighttime Thoughts

Overall, I had a (blank) type of day:

Did anything negative happen today?

How did I handle it and if I handled it negatively could I have done something different?

I can go to bed and think positive by doing the follow:

My nighttime positive affirmation is:

"I am healing"

Love yourself with the same intensity you want someone to love you with.

We crave to be loved by others. We want to feel wanted by others and sometimes even have crazy tendencies when we want someone to love us. We will go through hell and high waters to feel loved by someone else, often neglecting to love ourselves. You have to love yourself with the same intensity and energy that you want someone to love you with. Imagine if you put all of that love into yourself, how great of a person you will be? As well as identify ways that you already show yourself love.

I've learned that for the most part people love themselves but struggle with identifying what that looks like for them. For example, if you get sick the first thing you want to do is nurse yourself back to wellness. Even the smallest everyday task can be used as an identifier of how you show love to you. Start Identifying everyday small things that you do to show yourself love, so that you can begin to pour more into you.

As stated before, you have to love yourself with the same intensity that you want to love someone else. Be open to caring more about yourself, tending to your wellbeing, spending time alone, and remember to show up for yourself daily! That way, when someone does come along, you won't be looking for them to fill empty holes because you will be complete within yourself—everything after that will be a bonus.

"There's no going back to the old me because the new me is much better."

I HAVE TO POUR INTO ME
SO THAT I CAN BE
WHOLE
AND
COMPLETE

Morning Thoughts

Today, I woke up feeling like:

Today, in my healing process I want to unpack:

I can process this issue by doing:

I know that I cannot change anyone else and I only have the power to change myself. I can work on myself by doing the following:

A positive affirmation I can use throughout the day is:

Daytime Thoughts

Currently I feel:

Today, I am struggling with:

Coping mechanism and the people who supported me today:

Nighttime Thoughts

Overall, I had a (blank) type of day:

Did anything negative happen today?

How did I handle it and if I handled it negatively could I have done something different?

I can go to bed and think positive by doing the follow:

My nighttime positive affirmation is:

"I am healing"

Morning Thoughts

Today, I woke up feeling like:

Today, in my healing process I want to unpack:

I can process this issue by doing:

I know that I cannot change anyone else and I only have the power to change myself. I can work on myself by doing the following:

A positive affirmation I can use throughout the day is:

Daytime Thoughts

Currently I feel:

Today, I am struggling with:

Coping mechanism and the people who supported me today:

Nighttime Thoughts

Overall, I had a (blank) type of day:

Did anything negative happen today?

How did I handle it and if I handled it negatively could I have done something different?

I can go to bed and think positive by doing the follow:

My nighttime positive affirmation is:

"I am healing"

Morning Thoughts

Today, I woke up feeling like:

Today, in my healing process I want to unpack:

I can process this issue by doing:

I know that I cannot change anyone else and I only have the power to change myself. I can work on myself by doing the following:

A positive affirmation I can use throughout the day is:

Daytime Thoughts

Currently I feel:

Today, I am struggling with:

Coping mechanism and the people who supported me today:

Nighttime Thoughts

Overall, I had a (blank) type of day:

Did anything negative happen today?

How did I handle it and if I handled it negatively could I have done something different?

I can go to bed and think positive by doing the follow:

My nighttime positive affirmation is:

"I am healing"

Morning Thoughts

Date: /   /

Today, I woke up feeling like:

Today, in my healing process I want to unpack:

I can process this issue by doing:

I know that I cannot change anyone else and I only have the power to change myself. I can work on myself by doing the following:

A positive affirmation I can use throughout the day is:

Daytime Thoughts

Currently I feel:

Today, I am struggling with:

Coping mechanism and the people who supported me today:

Nighttime Thoughts

Overall, I had a (blank) type of day:

Did anything negative happen today?

How did I handle it and if I handled it negatively could I have done something different?

I can go to bed and think positive by doing the follow:

My nighttime positive affirmation is:

"I am healing"

Morning Thoughts

Today, I woke up feeling like:

Today, in my healing process I want to unpack:

I can process this issue by doing:

I know that I cannot change anyone else and I only have the power to change myself. I can work on myself by doing the following:

A positive affirmation I can use throughout the day is:

Daytime Thoughts

Currently I feel:

Today, I am struggling with:

Coping mechanism and the people who supported me today:

Nighttime Thoughts

Overall, I had a (blank) type of day:

Did anything negative happen today?

How did I handle it and if I handled it negatively could I have done something different?

I can go to bed and think positive by doing the follow:

My nighttime positive affirmation is:

"I am healing"

There are consequences for problematic behavior.

There's a saying out there that says, "Forgive and forget" but there's also a saying that says, "Fool me once, shame on you. Fool me twice, shame on me." Be mindful of how often you're validating people problematic behavior. Be willing to set healthy boundaries for others, so that they understand the power of consequences. People will only do to you what you allow them to do. Why allow others to take from you without it being your choice. Start handing out consequences (i.e., removing and/or taking a break from those who are problematic), so that you can heal and ensure your peace of mind is always intact. You have to teach people how to treat you. Start today with setting healthy boundaries for others. But most importantly make sure once the boundary is set that you follow through with handing out consequences for those who violate the boundaries you have put in place.

"Never apologize for choosing what's best for you."

Introspection

How can you hold other's accountable for their behaviors toward you?

_____

_____

_____

_____

_____

_____

_____

_____

_____

_____

_____

_____

_____

_____

_____

_____

_____

_____

Morning Thoughts

Today, I woke up feeling like:

Today, in my healing process I want to unpack:

I can process this issue by doing:

I know that I cannot change anyone else and I only have the power to change myself. I can work on myself by doing the following:

A positive affirmation I can use throughout the day is:

Daytime Thoughts

Currently I feel:

Today, I am struggling with:

Coping mechanism and the people who supported me today:

Nighttime Thoughts

Overall, I had a (blank) type of day:

Did anything negative happen today?

How did I handle it and if I handled it negatively could I have done something different?

I can go to bed and think positive by doing the follow:

My nighttime positive affirmation is:

"I am healing"

Morning Thoughts

Today, I woke up feeling like:

Today, in my healing process I want to unpack:

I can process this issue by doing:

I know that I cannot change anyone else and I only have the power to change myself. I can work on myself by doing the following:

A positive affirmation I can use throughout the day is:

Daytime Thoughts

Currently I feel:

Today, I am struggling with:

Coping mechanism and the people who supported me today:

Nighttime Thoughts

Overall, I had a (blank) type of day:

Did anything negative happen today?

How did I handle it and if I handled it negatively could I have done something different?

I can go to bed and think positive by doing the follow:

My nighttime positive affirmation is:

"I am healing"

Morning Thoughts

Date: /   /

Today, I woke up feeling like:

Today, in my healing process I want to unpack:

I can process this issue by doing:

I know that I cannot change anyone else and I only have the power to change myself. I can work on myself by doing the following:

A positive affirmation I can use throughout the day is:

Daytime Thoughts

Currently I feel:

Today, I am struggling with:

Coping mechanism and the people who supported me today:

Nighttime Thoughts

Overall, I had a (blank) type of day:

Did anything negative happen today?

How did I handle it and if I handled it negatively could I have done something different?

I can go to bed and think positive by doing the follow:

My nighttime positive affirmation is:

"I am healing"

Morning Thoughts

Today, I woke up feeling like:

Today, in my healing process I want to unpack:

I can process this issue by doing:

I know that I cannot change anyone else and I only have the power to change myself. I can work on myself by doing the following:

A positive affirmation I can use throughout the day is:

Daytime Thoughts

Currently I feel:

Today, I am struggling with:

Coping mechanism and the people who supported me today:

Nighttime Thoughts

Overall, I had a (blank) type of day:

Did anything negative happen today?

How did I handle it and if I handled it negatively could I have done something different?

I can go to bed and think positive by doing the follow:

My nighttime positive affirmation is:

"I am healing"

Morning Thoughts

Today, I woke up feeling like:

Today, in my healing process I want to unpack:

I can process this issue by doing:

I know that I cannot change anyone else and I only have the power to change myself.
I can work on myself by doing the following:

A positive affirmation I can use throughout the day is:

Daytime Thoughts

Currently I feel:

Today, I am struggling with:

Coping mechanism and the people who supported me today:

Nighttime Thoughts

Overall, I had a (blank) type of day:

Did anything negative happen today?

How did I handle it and if I handled it negatively could I have done something different?

I can go to bed and think positive by doing the follow:

My nighttime positive affirmation is:

"I am healing"

THINK IT, WRITE IT, HEAL IT

Healing

Don't apologize for the intent apologize for the impact.

Apologies come a dime a dozen. People know that you didn't intend to do whatever it is that you did. Whether at that moment it was intentional or not; but the impact is what's most damaging. It's not about what you did not intend to do, it's about how what you did impacted the other person. Start having conversations about the impact as oppose to the intent. Because just saying sorry at the time is not "enough". More often than not our actions can be more impactful than we may know.

Introspection

Talk about a time where you handled a situation wrong. How else could you have handled the situation? How did your actions impact the other person? What did you notice as a result of your actions? Try removing "why" from your statement and replace it with, "I feel" and discuss the impact.

_____

_____

_____

_____

_____

_____

_____

_____

_____

_____

_____

_____

_____

_____

_____

_____

_____

Morning Thoughts

Today, I woke up feeling like:

This issue is still bothering me from yesterday:

I choose to deal with yesterday's issue by doing:

Today, I am willing to let go of:

Today's self-care goal is:

A positive affirmation I can use throughout the day is:

Nighttime Thoughts

Overall, I had a _____ type of day. What was the good and the ugly of the day? Can those bad moments be turned into a good learning moment?

I have made the following changes in my life by:

The following are exactly what I need to do to continue to work on myself:

I know that I am healing because:

My nighttime takeaway for the day is?

"I am doing the work to be healed"

Morning Thoughts

Date: _____ / _____ / _____

Today, I woke up feeling like:

This issue is still bothering me from yesterday:

I choose to deal with yesterday's issue by doing:

Today, I am willing to let go of:

Today's self-care goal is:

A positive affirmation I can use throughout the day is:

Nighttime Thoughts

Overall, I had a _____ type of day. What was the good and the ugly of the day? Can those bad moments be turned into a good learning moment?

I have made the following changes in my life by:

The following are exactly what I need to do to continue to work on myself:

I know that I am healing because:

My nighttime takeaway for the day is?

"I am doing the work to be healed"

Morning Thoughts

Date: /   /

Today, I woke up feeling like:

This issue is still bothering me from yesterday:

I choose to deal with yesterday's issue by doing:

Today, I am willing to let go of:

Today's self-care goal is:

A positive affirmation I can use throughout the day is:

Nighttime Thoughts

Overall, I had a _____ type of day. What was the good and the ugly of the day? Can those bad moments be turned into a good learning moment?

I have made the following changes in my life by:

The following are exactly what I need to do to continue to work on myself:

I know that I am healing because:

My nighttime takeaway for the day is?

"I am doing the work to be healed"

Morning Thoughts

Date: /   /

Today, I woke up feeling like:

This issue is still bothering me from yesterday:

I choose to deal with yesterday's issue by doing:

Today, I am willing to let go of:

Today's self-care goal is:

A positive affirmation I can use throughout the day is:

Nighttime Thoughts

Overall, I had a _____ type of day. What was the good and the ugly of the day? Can those bad moments be turned into a good learning moment?

I have made the following changes in my life by:

The following are exactly what I need to do to continue to work on myself:

I know that I am healing because:

My nighttime takeaway for the day is?

"I am doing the work to be healed"

Morning Thoughts

Date: /   /

Today, I woke up feeling like:

This issue is still bothering me from yesterday:

I choose to deal with yesterday's issue by doing:

Today, I am willing to let go of:

Today's self-care goal is:

A positive affirmation I can use throughout the day is:

Nighttime Thoughts

Overall, I had a _____ type of day. What was the good and the ugly of the day? Can those bad moments be turned into a good learning moment?

I have made the following changes in my life by:

The following are exactly what I need to do to continue to work on myself:

I know that I am healing because:

My nighttime takeaway for the day is?

"I am doing the work to be healed"

Don't blame someone else for not understanding your feelings if you didn't articulate them well. They are not the problem you are!

People are not mind readers. They cannot know if they are doing something wrong if it isn't communicated effectively. Much of the time we want people to listen to what we have to say, when we want to say it, and how we want to say it but not everyone will be receptive, especially depending on the how and when. If you are having difficulties articulating your feelings, don't be upset with them for not understanding where you are coming from. You may need to find a way to communicate so that they can understand. Be mindful that they are a different person with a different mindset and experiences and they may not be in a mental space to receive a message from you. So, the work will have to be done starting with you, because that is where the healing will truly begin.

"I can't get over what I have to get through."

Introspection

Talk about your difficulties with communicating with others.

_____

_____

_____

_____

_____

_____

_____

_____

_____

_____

_____

_____

_____

_____

_____

_____

_____

_____

_____

Morning Thoughts

Date: /   /

Today, I woke up feeling like:

This issue is still bothering me from yesterday:

I choose to deal with yesterday's issue by doing:

Today, I am willing to let go of:

Today's self-care goal is:

A positive affirmation I can use throughout the day is:

Nighttime Thoughts

Overall, I had a _____ type of day. What was the good and the ugly of the day? Can those bad moments be turned into a good learning moment?

I have made the following changes in my life by:

The following are exactly what I need to do to continue to work on myself:

I know that I am healing because:

My nighttime takeaway for the day is?

"I am doing the work to be healed"

Morning Thoughts

Date: /   /

Today, I woke up feeling like:

This issue is still bothering me from yesterday:

I choose to deal with yesterday's issue by doing:

Today, I am willing to let go of:

Today's self-care goal is:

A positive affirmation I can use throughout the day is:

Nighttime Thoughts

Overall, I had a _____ type of day. What was the good and the ugly of the day? Can those bad moments be turned into a good learning moment?

I have made the following changes in my life by:

The following are exactly what I need to do to continue to work on myself:

I know that I am healing because:

My nighttime takeaway for the day is?

"I am doing the work to be healed"

Morning Thoughts

Date: ___ / ___ / ___

Today, I woke up feeling like:

This issue is still bothering me from yesterday:

I choose to deal with yesterday's issue by doing:

Today, I am willing to let go of:

Today's self-care goal is:

A positive affirmation I can use throughout the day is:

Nighttime Thoughts

Overall, I had a _____ type of day. What was the good and the ugly of the day? Can those bad moments be turned into a good learning moment?

I have made the following changes in my life by:

The following are exactly what I need to do to continue to work on myself:

I know that I am healing because:

My nighttime takeaway for the day is?

"I am doing the work to be healed"

Morning Thoughts

Date: /   /

Today, I woke up feeling like:

This issue is still bothering me from yesterday:

I choose to deal with yesterday's issue by doing:

Today, I am willing to let go of:

Today's self-care goal is:

A positive affirmation I can use throughout the day is:

Nighttime Thoughts

Overall, I had a _____ type of day. What was the good and the ugly of the day? Can those bad moments be turned into a good learning moment?

I have made the following changes in my life by:

The following are exactly what I need to do to continue to work on myself:

I know that I am healing because:

My nighttime takeaway for the day is?

"I am doing the work to be healed"

Morning Thoughts

Date: ___ / ___ / ___

Today, I woke up feeling like:

This issue is still bothering me from yesterday:

I choose to deal with yesterday's issue by doing:

Today, I am willing to let go of:

Today's self-care goal is:

A positive affirmation I can use throughout the day is:

Nighttime Thoughts

Overall, I had a _____ type of day. What was the good and the ugly of the day? Can those bad moments be turned into a good learning moment?

I have made the following changes in my life by:

The following are exactly what I need to do to continue to work on myself:

I know that I am healing because:

My nighttime takeaway for the day is?

"I am doing the work to be healed"

Everyone looks for honesty but when they receive it, they mistake it for something else!

How often do we ask people for their honesty? We even have phrases to express when we really want the truth such as: "Just be honest" or "Tell me the truth." Having others be honest with you is important but you must also remember that the other person's truth is just that, their truth from their perspective. We have to try harder as a whole to not mistake people's honesty for being rude, mean, angry, condescending, sarcastic, and or negative, because we didn't like what we heard on the receiving end, especially if we asked for it.

We have to be open enough to accept their feedback no matter how hurtful or angry they may make us. At least you'll know exactly how to deal with honesty better than you can a lie. Moreover, in the end you'll heal faster and move on quicker knowing the reality of how you are being perceived by others in that situation.

Introspection

Has honest criticism ever bothered you? What was it that bothered you the most about what someone else's truth about you were?

_____

_____

_____

_____

_____

_____

_____

_____

_____

_____

_____

_____

_____

_____

_____

_____

_____

_____

Morning Thoughts

Date: /   /

Today, I woke up feeling like:

This issue is still bothering me from yesterday:

I choose to deal with yesterday's issue by doing:

Today, I am willing to let go of:

Today's self-care goal is:

A positive affirmation I can use throughout the day is:

Nighttime Thoughts

Overall, I had a _____ type of day. What was the good and the ugly of the day? Can those bad moments be turned into a good learning moment?

I have made the following changes in my life by:

The following are exactly what I need to do to continue to work on myself:

I know that I am healing because:

My nighttime takeaway for the day is?

"I am doing the work to be healed"

Morning Thoughts

Date: ___ / ___ / ___

Today, I woke up feeling like:

This issue is still bothering me from yesterday:

I choose to deal with yesterday's issue by doing:

Today, I am willing to let go of:

Today's self-care goal is:

A positive affirmation I can use throughout the day is:

Nighttime Thoughts

Overall, I had a _____ type of day. What was the good and the ugly of the day? Can those bad moments be turned into a good learning moment?

I have made the following changes in my life by:

The following are exactly what I need to do to continue to work on myself:

I know that I am healing because:

My nighttime takeaway for the day is?

"I am doing the work to be healed"

Morning Thoughts

Date: /   /

Today, I woke up feeling like:

This issue is still bothering me from yesterday:

I choose to deal with yesterday's issue by doing:

Today, I am willing to let go of:

Today's self-care goal is:

A positive affirmation I can use throughout the day is:

Nighttime Thoughts

Overall, I had a _____ type of day. What was the good and the ugly of the day? Can those bad moments be turned into a good learning moment?

I have made the following changes in my life by:

The following are exactly what I need to do to continue to work on myself:

I know that I am healing because:

My nighttime takeaway for the day is?

"I am doing the work to be healed"

Morning Thoughts

Today, I woke up feeling like:

This issue is still bothering me from yesterday:

I choose to deal with yesterday's issue by doing:

Today, I am willing to let go of:

Today's self-care goal is:

A positive affirmation I can use throughout the day is:

Nighttime Thoughts

Overall, I had a _____ type of day. What was the good and the ugly of the day? Can those bad moments be turned into a good learning moment?

I have made the following changes in my life by:

The following are exactly what I need to do to continue to work on myself:

I know that I am healing because:

My nighttime takeaway for the day is?

"I am doing the work to be healed"

Morning Thoughts

Date: / /

Today, I woke up feeling like:

This issue is still bothering me from yesterday:

I choose to deal with yesterday's issue by doing:

Today, I am willing to let go of:

Today's self-care goal is:

A positive affirmation I can use throughout the day is:

Nighttime Thoughts

Overall, I had a _____ type of day. What was the good and the ugly of the day? Can those bad moments be turned into a good learning moment?

I have made the following changes in my life by:

The following are exactly what I need to do to continue to work on myself:

I know that I am healing because:

My nighttime takeaway for the day is?

"I am doing the work to be healed"

Stop blaming yourself for other people character flaws. Your only responsibility is how you respond to what you have been handed.

D on't let someone guilt you into blaming yourself for their negative behavior. Stand firm on how you feel and make the necessary changes, and never let someone guilt you into being the person in the wrong when they are the problem. Stand firm and choose you!

Introspection

How can you stand on your decisions and choose what's best for you?

_____

_____

_____

_____

_____

_____

_____

_____

_____

_____

_____

_____

_____

_____

_____

_____

_____

_____

_____

Morning Thoughts

Date: /   /

Today, I woke up feeling like:

This issue is still bothering me from yesterday:

I choose to deal with yesterday's issue by doing:

Today, I am willing to let go of:

Today's self-care goal is:

A positive affirmation I can use throughout the day is:

Nighttime Thoughts

Overall, I had a _____ type of day. What was the good and the ugly of the day? Can those bad moments be turned into a good learning moment?

I have made the following changes in my life by:

The following are exactly what I need to do to continue to work on myself:

I know that I am healing because:

My nighttime takeaway for the day is?

"I am doing the work to be healed"

Morning Thoughts

Today, I woke up feeling like:

This issue is still bothering me from yesterday:

I choose to deal with yesterday's issue by doing:

Today, I am willing to let go of:

Today's self-care goal is:

A positive affirmation I can use throughout the day is:

Nighttime Thoughts

Overall, I had a _____ type of day. What was the good and the ugly of the day? Can those bad moments be turned into a good learning moment?

I have made the following changes in my life by:

The following are exactly what I need to do to continue to work on myself:

I know that I am healing because:

My nighttime takeaway for the day is?

"I am doing the work to be healed"

Morning Thoughts

Date: /   /

Today, I woke up feeling like:

This issue is still bothering me from yesterday:

I choose to deal with yesterday's issue by doing:

Today, I am willing to let go of:

Today's self-care goal is:

A positive affirmation I can use throughout the day is:

Nighttime Thoughts

Overall, I had a _____ type of day. What was the good and the ugly of the day? Can those bad moments be turned into a good learning moment?

I have made the following changes in my life by:

The following are exactly what I need to do to continue to work on myself:

I know that I am healing because:

My nighttime takeaway for the day is?

"I am doing the work to be healed"

Morning Thoughts

Today, I woke up feeling like:

This issue is still bothering me from yesterday:

I choose to deal with yesterday's issue by doing:

Today, I am willing to let go of:

Today's self-care goal is:

A positive affirmation I can use throughout the day is:

Nighttime Thoughts

Overall, I had a _____ type of day. What was the good and the ugly of the day? Can those bad moments be turned into a good learning moment?

I have made the following changes in my life by:

The following are exactly what I need to do to continue to work on myself:

I know that I am healing because:

My nighttime takeaway for the day is?

"I am doing the work to be healed"

Morning Thoughts

Date: /   /

Today, I woke up feeling like:

This issue is still bothering me from yesterday:

I choose to deal with yesterday's issue by doing:

Today, I am willing to let go of:

Today's self-care goal is:

A positive affirmation I can use throughout the day is:

Nighttime Thoughts

Overall, I had a _____ type of day. What was the good and the ugly of the day? Can those bad moments be turned into a good learning moment?

I have made the following changes in my life by:

The following are exactly what I need to do to continue to work on myself:

I know that I am healing because:

My nighttime takeaway for the day is?

"I am doing the work to be healed"

Introspection

5 Things I need to release to heal

1.

2.

3.

4.

5.

Introspection

5 things that can contribute to my personal growth

1.

2.

3.

4.

5.

Morning Thoughts

Date: ___ / ___ / ___

Today, I woke up feeling like:

This issue is still bothering me from yesterday:

I choose to deal with yesterday's issue by doing:

Today, I am willing to let go of:

Today's self-care goal is:

A positive affirmation I can use throughout the day is:

Nighttime Thoughts

Overall, I had a _____ type of day. What was the good and the ugly of the day? Can those bad moments be turned into a good learning moment?

I have made the following changes in my life by:

The following are exactly what I need to do to continue to work on myself:

I know that I am healing because:

My nighttime takeaway for the day is?

"I am doing the work to be healed"

Morning Thoughts

Date: /   /

Today, I woke up feeling like:

This issue is still bothering me from yesterday:

I choose to deal with yesterday's issue by doing:

Today, I am willing to let go of:

Today's self-care goal is:

A positive affirmation I can use throughout the day is:

Nighttime Thoughts

Overall, I had a _____ type of day. What was the good and the ugly of the day? Can those bad moments be turned into a good learning moment?

I have made the following changes in my life by:

The following are exactly what I need to do to continue to work on myself:

I know that I am healing because:

My nighttime takeaway for the day is?

"I am doing the work to be healed"

Morning Thoughts

Today, I woke up feeling like:

This issue is still bothering me from yesterday:

I choose to deal with yesterday's issue by doing:

Today, I am willing to let go of:

Today's self-care goal is:

A positive affirmation I can use throughout the day is:

Nighttime Thoughts

Overall, I had a _____ type of day. What was the good and the ugly of the day? Can those bad moments be turned into a good learning moment?

I have made the following changes in my life by:

The following are exactly what I need to do to continue to work on myself:

I know that I am healing because:

My nighttime takeaway for the day is?

"I am doing the work to be healed"

Morning Thoughts

Date: /   /

Today, I woke up feeling like:

This issue is still bothering me from yesterday:

I choose to deal with yesterday's issue by doing:

Today, I am willing to let go of:

Today's self-care goal is:

A positive affirmation I can use throughout the day is:

Nighttime Thoughts

Overall, I had a _____ type of day. What was the good and the ugly of the day? Can those bad moments be turned into a good learning moment?

I have made the following changes in my life by:

The following are exactly what I need to do to continue to work on myself:

I know that I am healing because:

My nighttime takeaway for the day is?

"I am doing the work to be healed"

Morning Thoughts

Date: /   /

Today, I woke up feeling like:

This issue is still bothering me from yesterday:

I choose to deal with yesterday's issue by doing:

Today, I am willing to let go of:

Today's self-care goal is:

A positive affirmation I can use throughout the day is:

Nighttime Thoughts

Overall, I had a _____ type of day. What was the good and the ugly of the day? Can those bad moments be turned into a good learning moment?

I have made the following changes in my life by:

The following are exactly what I need to do to continue to work on myself:

I know that I am healing because:

My nighttime takeaway for the day is?

"I am doing the work to be healed"

Healing is about honesty, you can't heal what you're not willing to face with an honest open heart. Live in your truth and be clear about what your intentions are.

As ugly as your truth may be, you can't run from it. You have to be willing to face yourself with honesty to truly heal what's broken. Healing starts with you. You can't heal what is broken if you're not willing to be honest and truthful with yourself.

"I owe it to myself to keep fighting."

Introspection

Do you have any difficulties with being honest with yourself?
Why or why not?

_____

_____

_____

_____

_____

_____

_____

_____

What is an ugly truth that you may be running from?

_____

_____

_____

_____

_____

_____

_____

_____

Morning Thoughts

Today, I woke up feeling like:

This issue is still bothering me from yesterday:

I choose to deal with yesterday's issue by doing:

Today, I am willing to let go of:

Today's self-care goal is:

A positive affirmation I can use throughout the day is:

Nighttime Thoughts

Overall, I had a _____ type of day. What was the good and the ugly of the day? Can those bad moments be turned into a good learning moment?

I have made the following changes in my life by:

The following are exactly what I need to do to continue to work on myself:

I know that I am healing because:

My nighttime takeaway for the day is?

"I am doing the work to be healed"

Morning Thoughts

Date: /   /

Today, I woke up feeling like:

This issue is still bothering me from yesterday:

I choose to deal with yesterday's issue by doing:

Today, I am willing to let go of:

Today's self-care goal is:

A positive affirmation I can use throughout the day is:

Nighttime Thoughts

Overall, I had a _____ type of day. What was the good and the ugly of the day? Can those bad moments be turned into a good learning moment?

I have made the following changes in my life by:

The following are exactly what I need to do to continue to work on myself:

I know that I am healing because:

My nighttime takeaway for the day is?

"I am doing the work to be healed"

Morning Thoughts

Today, I woke up feeling like:

This issue is still bothering me from yesterday:

I choose to deal with yesterday's issue by doing:

Today, I am willing to let go of:

Today's self-care goal is:

A positive affirmation I can use throughout the day is:

Nighttime Thoughts

Overall, I had a _____ type of day. What was the good and the ugly of the day? Can those bad moments be turned into a good learning moment?

I have made the following changes in my life by:

The following are exactly what I need to do to continue to work on myself:

I know that I am healing because:

My nighttime takeaway for the day is?

"I am doing the work to be healed"

Morning Thoughts

Date: /   /

Today, I woke up feeling like:

This issue is still bothering me from yesterday:

I choose to deal with yesterday's issue by doing:

Today, I am willing to let go of:

Today's self-care goal is:

A positive affirmation I can use throughout the day is:

Nighttime Thoughts

Overall, I had a _____ type of day. What was the good and the ugly of the day? Can those bad moments be turned into a good learning moment?

I have made the following changes in my life by:

The following are exactly what I need to do to continue to work on myself:

I know that I am healing because:

My nighttime takeaway for the day is?

"I am doing the work to be healed"

Morning Thoughts

Today, I woke up feeling like:

This issue is still bothering me from yesterday:

I choose to deal with yesterday's issue by doing:

Today, I am willing to let go of:

Today's self-care goal is:

A positive affirmation I can use throughout the day is:

Nighttime Thoughts

Overall, I had a _____ type of day. What was the good and the ugly of the day? Can those bad moments be turned into a good learning moment?

I have made the following changes in my life by:

The following are exactly what I need to do to continue to work on myself:

I know that I am healing because:

My nighttime takeaway for the day is?

"I am doing the work to be healed"

Self-Care and Coping Skills:
Take What You Need

- [ ] Get more adequate sleep
- [ ] Exercise
- [ ] Eat healthy food
- [ ] Laugh more
- [ ] Positive self-talk and positive attitude
- [ ] Talk to people you trust
- [ ] Work at managing your time
- [ ] Make an effort to relax
- [ ] Use a weighted blanket or snuggle under a cozy blanket
- [ ] Take a hot shower or a warm bath.
- [ ] Get a massage
- [ ] Pay attention to your breathing
- [ ] Burn a scented candle.
- [ ] Listen to music
- [ ] Take yourself out to eat.
- [ ] Explore your town
- [ ] Garden
- [ ] Watch a movie.
- [ ] Make art. Do a craft project.
- [ ] Journal
- [ ] Clean out a junk drawer or a closet.
- [ ] Try a new activity.

- [ ] Work on short term goals
- [ ] Read something on a topic you wouldn't normally.
- [ ] Read poetry or inspiring quotes.
- [ ] Light a candle.
- [ ] Meditate
- [ ] Spend time in nature.
- [ ] Pray.
- [ ] List things you're grateful for.
- [ ] Accept your feelings.
- [ ] They are natural human emotions.
- [ ] Write your feelings down.
- [ ] Cry when you need to.
- [ ] Be kind to yourself
- [ ] Dance.
- [ ] Stretch
- [ ] Go for a bike ride.
- [ ] Don't skip sleep to get things done.
- [ ] Take a nap.
- [ ] Go on a lunch date with a friend.
- [ ] Call a friend on the phone
- [ ] Participate in a book club
- [ ] Join a support group.

I PRAY YOU HEAL
FROM THING
NO ONE EVER
APOLOGIZED FOR.

- Nakeia Homer

Morning Thoughts

Date: /   /

Today, I woke up feeling like:

This issue is still bothering me from yesterday:

I choose to deal with yesterday's issue by doing:

Today, I am willing to let go of:

Today's self-care goal is:

A positive affirmation I can use throughout the day is:

Nighttime Thoughts

Overall, I had a _____ type of day. What was the good and the ugly of the day? Can those bad moments be turned into a good learning moment?

I have made the following changes in my life by:

The following are exactly what I need to do to continue to work on myself:

I know that I am healing because:

My nighttime takeaway for the day is?

"I am doing the work to be healed"

Morning Thoughts

Today, I woke up feeling like:

This issue is still bothering me from yesterday:

I choose to deal with yesterday's issue by doing:

Today, I am willing to let go of:

Today's self-care goal is:

A positive affirmation I can use throughout the day is:

Nighttime Thoughts

Overall, I had a _____ type of day. What was the good and the ugly of the day? Can those bad moments be turned into a good learning moment?

I have made the following changes in my life by:

The following are exactly what I need to do to continue to work on myself:

I know that I am healing because:

My nighttime takeaway for the day is?

"I am doing the work to be healed"

Morning Thoughts

Today, I woke up feeling like:

This issue is still bothering me from yesterday:

I choose to deal with yesterday's issue by doing:

Today, I am willing to let go of:

Today's self-care goal is:

A positive affirmation I can use throughout the day is:

Nighttime Thoughts

Overall, I had a _____ type of day. What was the good and the ugly of the day? Can those bad moments be turned into a good learning moment?

I have made the following changes in my life by:

The following are exactly what I need to do to continue to work on myself:

I know that I am healing because:

My nighttime takeaway for the day is?

"I am doing the work to be healed"

Morning Thoughts

Today, I woke up feeling like:

This issue is still bothering me from yesterday:

I choose to deal with yesterday's issue by doing:

Today, I am willing to let go of:

Today's self-care goal is:

A positive affirmation I can use throughout the day is:

Nighttime Thoughts

Overall, I had a _____ type of day. What was the good and the ugly of the day? Can those bad moments be turned into a good learning moment?

I have made the following changes in my life by:

The following are exactly what I need to do to continue to work on myself:

I know that I am healing because:

My nighttime takeaway for the day is?

"I am doing the work to be healed"

Morning Thoughts

Date: /   /

Today, I woke up feeling like:

This issue is still bothering me from yesterday:

I choose to deal with yesterday's issue by doing:

Today, I am willing to let go of:

Today's self-care goal is:

A positive affirmation I can use throughout the day is:

Nighttime Thoughts

Overall, I had a _____ type of day. What was the good and the ugly of the day? Can those bad moments be turned into a good learning moment?

I have made the following changes in my life by:

The following are exactly what I need to do to continue to work on myself:

I know that I am healing because:

My nighttime takeaway for the day is?

"I am doing the work to be healed"

I've learned that one of the hardest things for people to do is take accountability for their own actions.

It's so easy to blame others for things that happened in our lives as a means for justification and validation of our feelings and actions. When we can remove the other person from the equation and take a long hard look at self, you can find so much truth, growth, and power within you. Everybody plays a part in the game called life. Focus on what your role is and how you can evolve daily. Take accountability without beating yourself up for mistakes and errors that you have made. Welcome mistakes and grow from them, heal from them, and learn from them.

"I began to heal once I stopped blaming you."

Introspection

How can you take accountability and ownership for the role you may have caused as a result of being broken?

_____

_____

_____

_____

_____

_____

_____

_____

_____

_____

_____

_____

_____

_____

_____

_____

_____

_____

Morning Thoughts

Date: /   /

Today, I woke up feeling like:

This issue is still bothering me from yesterday:

I choose to deal with yesterday's issue by doing:

Today, I am willing to let go of:

Today's self-care goal is:

A positive affirmation I can use throughout the day is:

Nighttime Thoughts

Overall, I had a _____ type of day. What was the good and the ugly of the day? Can those bad moments be turned into a good learning moment?

I have made the following changes in my life by:

The following are exactly what I need to do to continue to work on myself:

I know that I am healing because:

My nighttime takeaway for the day is?

"I am doing the work to be healed"

Morning Thoughts

Date: /   /

Today, I woke up feeling like:

This issue is still bothering me from yesterday:

I choose to deal with yesterday's issue by doing:

Today, I am willing to let go of:

Today's self-care goal is:

A positive affirmation I can use throughout the day is:

Nighttime Thoughts

Overall, I had a _____ type of day. What was the good and the ugly of the day? Can those bad moments be turned into a good learning moment?

I have made the following changes in my life by:

The following are exactly what I need to do to continue to work on myself:

I know that I am healing because:

My nighttime takeaway for the day is?

"I am doing the work to be healed"

Morning Thoughts

Today, I woke up feeling like:

This issue is still bothering me from yesterday:

I choose to deal with yesterday's issue by doing:

Today, I am willing to let go of:

Today's self-care goal is:

A positive affirmation I can use throughout the day is:

Nighttime Thoughts

Overall, I had a _____ type of day. What was the good and the ugly of the day? Can those bad moments be turned into a good learning moment?

I have made the following changes in my life by:

The following are exactly what I need to do to continue to work on myself:

I know that I am healing because:

My nighttime takeaway for the day is?

"I am doing the work to be healed"

Morning Thoughts

Today, I woke up feeling like:

This issue is still bothering me from yesterday:

I choose to deal with yesterday's issue by doing:

Today, I am willing to let go of:

Today's self-care goal is:

A positive affirmation I can use throughout the day is:

Nighttime Thoughts

Overall, I had a _____ type of day. What was the good and the ugly of the day? Can those bad moments be turned into a good learning moment?

I have made the following changes in my life by:

The following are exactly what I need to do to continue to work on myself:

I know that I am healing because:

My nighttime takeaway for the day is?

"I am doing the work to be healed"

Morning Thoughts

Today, I woke up feeling like:

This issue is still bothering me from yesterday:

I choose to deal with yesterday's issue by doing:

Today, I am willing to let go of:

Today's self-care goal is:

A positive affirmation I can use throughout the day is:

Nighttime Thoughts

Overall, I had a _____ type of day. What was the good and the ugly of the day? Can those bad moments be turned into a good learning moment?

I have made the following changes in my life by:

The following are exactly what I need to do to continue to work on myself:

I know that I am healing because:

My nighttime takeaway for the day is?

"I am doing the work to be healed"

Don't be bitter, get better.

Be mindful of the energy you put out in the world about things you've lost. That negative energy often attracts more negativity to enter your mind. It also shows just how much dependence you may have put into someone or something else. Instead you should be the greatness in other people's lives as opposed to depending on them being the best thing in your life. Remember, when you lose someone or something then there is a good chance that it wasn't meant for you to have or hold onto. So why be bitter about moving on as now you have a chance to possibly find something greater? Why be angry about how someone treated you? That's like being mad about planting seeds when the soil was rock hard to begin with. Truth is, not many people are honest about their loss or good at letting go. You need to be real about your role in the situation, enough to realize that that person or thing felt like only great thing in my life because you didn't love yourself enough to know that you are worthy to be loved abundantly and correctly. When I started my own journey, I didn't know that my love exists from within and not from what someone else has given me either. Bitter and angry is the person who wasn't great for themselves and expected it from someone else. Now you are left to mourn the loss what you thought you were receiving from someone else that you couldn't give yourself. Start the healing process, be honest with yourself, love yourself, and allow yourself to grow.

"No matter what I will win."

Introspection

What is it that you need to do right now and how can you move forward in such a way it doesn't require dependence on anyone or anything other than yourself?

_____

_____

_____

_____

_____

_____

_____

_____

_____

_____

_____

_____

_____

_____

Note: if that need does require a counselor, therapist, or psychologist, that is perfectly okay to seek professional help as well. Just try to avoid using your personal relationships.

Morning Thoughts

Date: /   /

Today, I woke up feeling like:

This issue is still bothering me from yesterday:

I choose to deal with yesterday's issue by doing:

Today, I am willing to let go of:

Today's self-care goal is:

A positive affirmation I can use throughout the day is:

Nighttime Thoughts

Overall, I had a _____ type of day. What was the good and the ugly of the day? Can those bad moments be turned into a good learning moment?

I have made the following changes in my life by:

The following are exactly what I need to do to continue to work on myself:

I know that I am healing because:

My nighttime takeaway for the day is?

"I am doing the work to be healed"

Morning Thoughts

Today, I woke up feeling like:

This issue is still bothering me from yesterday:

I choose to deal with yesterday's issue by doing:

Today, I am willing to let go of:

Today's self-care goal is:

A positive affirmation I can use throughout the day is:

Nighttime Thoughts

Overall, I had a _____ type of day. What was the good and the ugly of the day? Can those bad moments be turned into a good learning moment?

I have made the following changes in my life by:

The following are exactly what I need to do to continue to work on myself:

I know that I am healing because:

My nighttime takeaway for the day is?

"I am doing the work to be healed"

Morning Thoughts

Today, I woke up feeling like:

This issue is still bothering me from yesterday:

I choose to deal with yesterday's issue by doing:

Today, I am willing to let go of:

Today's self-care goal is:

A positive affirmation I can use throughout the day is:

Nighttime Thoughts

Overall, I had a _____ type of day. What was the good and the ugly of the day? Can those bad moments be turned into a good learning moment?

I have made the following changes in my life by:

The following are exactly what I need to do to continue to work on myself:

I know that I am healing because:

My nighttime takeaway for the day is?

Morning Thoughts

Today, I woke up feeling like:

This issue is still bothering me from yesterday:

I choose to deal with yesterday's issue by doing:

Today, I am willing to let go of:

Today's self-care goal is:

A positive affirmation I can use throughout the day is:

Nighttime Thoughts

Overall, I had a _____ type of day. What was the good and the ugly of the day? Can those bad moments be turned into a good learning moment?

I have made the following changes in my life by:

The following are exactly what I need to do to continue to work on myself:

I know that I am healing because:

My nighttime takeaway for the day is?

"I am doing the work to be healed"

Morning Thoughts

Today, I woke up feeling like:

This issue is still bothering me from yesterday:

I choose to deal with yesterday's issue by doing:

Today, I am willing to let go of:

Today's self-care goal is:

A positive affirmation I can use throughout the day is:

Nighttime Thoughts

Overall, I had a _____ type of day. What was the good and the ugly of the day? Can those bad moments be turned into a good learning moment?

I have made the following changes in my life by:

The following are exactly what I need to do to continue to work on myself:

I know that I am healing because:

My nighttime takeaway for the day is?

"I am doing the work to be healed"

You gotta keep going!

You gotta keep going! Don't give up. I know it can be easy to do. But focus on what's in front of you and not what's behind or to the side of you. If you keep one foot in front of the other, even if you gotta take baby steps, you will come out on top. Life hands us challenges, it's what we do with those challenges that mean something. So keep going, even when it looks like you're not winning! You are! And your lane in life is set specifically for you, so keep on going.

"I don't know how I am going to make it through but just know I am going to make it through."

I've been searching for me! And I've finally found myself! And it feels great!

Morning Thoughts

Date: /   /

Today, I woke up feeling like:

This issue is still bothering me from yesterday:

I choose to deal with yesterday's issue by doing:

Today, I am willing to let go of:

Today's self-care goal is:

A positive affirmation I can use throughout the day is:

Nighttime Thoughts

Overall, I had a _____ type of day. What was the good and the ugly of the day? Can those bad moments be turned into a good learning moment?

I have made the following changes in my life by:

The following are exactly what I need to do to continue to work on myself:

I know that I am healing because:

My nighttime takeaway for the day is?

"I am doing the work to be healed"

Morning Thoughts

Today, I woke up feeling like:

This issue is still bothering me from yesterday:

I choose to deal with yesterday's issue by doing:

Today, I am willing to let go of:

Today's self-care goal is:

A positive affirmation I can use throughout the day is:

Nighttime Thoughts

Overall, I had a _____ type of day. What was the good and the ugly of the day? Can those bad moments be turned into a good learning moment?

I have made the following changes in my life by:

The following are exactly what I need to do to continue to work on myself:

I know that I am healing because:

My nighttime takeaway for the day is?

"I am doing the work to be healed"

Morning Thoughts

Today, I woke up feeling like:

This issue is still bothering me from yesterday:

I choose to deal with yesterday's issue by doing:

Today, I am willing to let go of:

Today's self-care goal is:

A positive affirmation I can use throughout the day is:

Nighttime Thoughts

Overall, I had a _____ type of day. What was the good and the ugly of the day? Can those bad moments be turned into a good learning moment?

I have made the following changes in my life by:

The following are exactly what I need to do to continue to work on myself:

I know that I am healing because:

My nighttime takeaway for the day is?

"I am doing the work to be healed"

Morning Thoughts

Today, I woke up feeling like:

This issue is still bothering me from yesterday:

I choose to deal with yesterday's issue by doing:

Today, I am willing to let go of:

Today's self-care goal is:

A positive affirmation I can use throughout the day is:

Nighttime Thoughts

Overall, I had a _____ type of day. What was the good and the ugly of the day? Can those bad moments be turned into a good learning moment?

I have made the following changes in my life by:

The following are exactly what I need to do to continue to work on myself:

I know that I am healing because:

My nighttime takeaway for the day is?

"I am doing the work to be healed"

Morning Thoughts

Today, I woke up feeling like:

This issue is still bothering me from yesterday:

I choose to deal with yesterday's issue by doing:

Today, I am willing to let go of:

Today's self-care goal is:

A positive affirmation I can use throughout the day is:

Nighttime Thoughts

Overall, I had a _____ type of day. What was the good and the ugly of the day? Can those bad moments be turned into a good learning moment?

I have made the following changes in my life by:

The following are exactly what I need to do to continue to work on myself:

I know that I am healing because:

My nighttime takeaway for the day is?

"I am doing the work to be healed"

Make yourself a priority.

It's never too late to say yes to you! I challenge you each week, to do something nice for yourself. Whether that's cooking your favorite meal to a spa date, or catching up on your favorite tv show. Do something for you, have some uninterrupted time to be free from the outside world and focus on you! Self-care is important. Internal and external checkups are essential in this life. Self-care starts with you.

"There's no rush to healing. Take all the time
you need to heal."

Introspection

Identify below at least three internal and three external self-care practices. Can you implement these things into your daily routine? If so how would you do so? (Tell me your plan).

_____

_____

_____

_____

_____

_____

_____

_____

_____

_____

_____

_____

_____

_____

_____

_____

_____

Morning Thoughts

Today, I woke up feeling like:

,

This issue is still bothering me from yesterday:

I choose to deal with yesterday's issue by doing:

Today, I am willing to let go of:

Today's self-care goal is:

A positive affirmation I can use throughout the day is:

Nighttime Thoughts

Overall, I had a _____ type of day. What was the good and the ugly of the day? Can those bad moments be turned into a good learning moment?

I have made the following changes in my life by:

The following are exactly what I need to do to continue to work on myself:

I know that I am healing because:

My nighttime takeaway for the day is?

"I am doing the work to be healed"

Morning Thoughts

Date: /   /

Today, I woke up feeling like:

This issue is still bothering me from yesterday:

I choose to deal with yesterday's issue by doing:

Today, I am willing to let go of:

Today's self-care goal is:

A positive affirmation I can use throughout the day is:

Nighttime Thoughts

Overall, I had a _____ type of day. What was the good and the ugly of the day? Can those bad moments be turned into a good learning moment?

I have made the following changes in my life by:

The following are exactly what I need to do to continue to work on myself:

I know that I am healing because:

My nighttime takeaway for the day is?

"I am doing the work to be healed"

Morning Thoughts

Today, I woke up feeling like:

This issue is still bothering me from yesterday:

I choose to deal with yesterday's issue by doing:

Today, I am willing to let go of:

Today's self-care goal is:

A positive affirmation I can use throughout the day is:

Nighttime Thoughts

Overall, I had a _____ type of day. What was the good and the ugly of the day? Can those bad moments be turned into a good learning moment?

I have made the following changes in my life by:

The following are exactly what I need to do to continue to work on myself:

I know that I am healing because:

My nighttime takeaway for the day is?

"I am doing the work to be healed"

Morning Thoughts

Today, I woke up feeling like:

This issue is still bothering me from yesterday:

I choose to deal with yesterday's issue by doing:

Today, I am willing to let go of:

Today's self-care goal is:

A positive affirmation I can use throughout the day is:

Nighttime Thoughts

Overall, I had a _____ type of day. What was the good and the ugly of the day? Can those bad moments be turned into a good learning moment?

I have made the following changes in my life by:

The following are exactly what I need to do to continue to work on myself:

I know that I am healing because:

My nighttime takeaway for the day is?

"I am doing the work to be healed"

Morning Thoughts

Date: /   /

Today, I woke up feeling like:

This issue is still bothering me from yesterday:

I choose to deal with yesterday's issue by doing:

Today, I am willing to let go of:

Today's self-care goal is:

A positive affirmation I can use throughout the day is:

Nighttime Thoughts

Overall, I had a _____ type of day. What was the good and the ugly of the day? Can those bad moments be turned into a good learning moment?

I have made the following changes in my life by:

The following are exactly what I need to do to continue to work on myself:

I know that I am healing because:

My nighttime takeaway for the day is?

"I am doing the work to be healed"

I AM
A WORK OF
ART,
A MASTERPIECE